ATED THE HEAVEN AND THE

WITHOUT FORM AND VOID

The Holy

AT THE

A revision and an expansion of the 1960 catalogue,
The Holy Bible, An Exhibit, by Edwin T. Bowden.

Bible

by David R. Farmer

UNIVERSITY OF TEXAS

Published by The Humanities Research Center, The University of Texas, Austin, Texas

Printed and bound in the United States of America

T WOULD BE DIFFICULT TO name a group of books that has any broader value for a humanities research center than a collection of Bibles. The opportunities they offer for research are wide and varied: study of the scriptures themselves is, of course, of the first importance, aided by the various texts and translations available in a large collection. The different translations and the often involved printing history of individual editions lead the scholar also into the study of church history. The French New Testament of 1667, The Port Royal version, for instance, names Gaspard Migeot of Mons as the printer but was probably printed by Daniel Elzevier at Amsterdam because of the official church opposition to the Jansenist De Sacy translation. Similarly, the first Roman Catholic New Testament in English was published at Rhemes in 1582 rather than in England; according to Lord Burleigh anyone in possession of a copy in English was subject to imprisonment and anyone caught circulating the edition was to be punished by torture.

The importance of Bibles in the study of intellectual and even political history is a necessary corollary of their importance to religious history; the various compartments of history find a common corridor here. Tyndale's translation of 1382 was a historical event that touched every element of English history. But the secular study of the various Bibles is not limited to historians alone. The influence of particular translations on theories of government and economics and sociology and law offers a wide field of research. The student of literature and language must find the influence of the various translations of particular interest, often as great as the literary value of the translation itself. The English translation of 1611, the "King James" or "authorized" edition, for instance, has had an enormous effect on the language we speak and the books we read and admire. Or again, the student of our own early Puritan literature must always take into consideration the Puritans' preference for the Geneva rather than the King James translation.

Bibles offer too an opportunity for research in bibliography and the history of printing. After all, the Gutenberg Bible of the 1450's was—or at least most scholars think it was—the first complete, existing book printed by movable type in the western world. Since then the Bible has certainly been the most often printed book. Bibliographies are still far from complete, and much bibliographical investigation, even on famous editions, still remains to be done. Smaller problems are common: which of the London duodecimos of 1658, for instance, is the genuine and which the foreign or pirated edition? Exactly when and where were the Geneva quartos of 1599 printed? Such problems may not be of great importance, but they are of some interest and provide the university student of bibliography a chance to try his hand. For those interested in printing as a fine art, early Bibles provide notable examples and lead up to such masterpieces as John Baskerville's folio of 1763 or the twentieth century Doves Press edition in five volumes. Perhaps there is even something to be done here in the history of taste in western European civilization; certainly the extra-illustrated Bibles in the Research Center provide pertinent material.

The variety of research opportunities offered by the Bible creates a special problem in selecting particular copies for an exhibition. The problem is made greater too by the fact that in the past the Humanities Research Center has made no special effort to collect Bibles. Most of those it has—and they are a good many—are simply the ones that have appeared in the various other collections of books that represent in such large part the holdings of the Center. The Parsons collection, for instance, is particularly fruitful here. One exception deserves mention: the small but rich collection of Bibles presented to the University by Mr. H. L. Williford of Dallas provides a fine nucleus for a larger collection of the future. It is hoped that from now on this nucleus can be expanded into a full-scale, relatively complete collection.

Another problem arises too in the question of what should be included in the general category of "Bible." Many prayer books and books of church ritual and spiritual exercise are obviously closely related and often contain extensive quotation from the Bible. Similarly many books of comment and exegesis reproduce in part or in whole the applicable sections of the full Bible. One of the most popular of all books has long been the Book of Psalms in original translation, often poetical or even set to music. A great many of the early English Bibles, for instance, are bound with one of the numerous early editions of *The Whole Booke of Psalmes, Collected into English Meetre, by Thomas Sternhold, John Hopkins, and Others . . . with Apt Notes to Sing Them Withall*. These seem properly to belong in the category, since they are translations of a clear segment of the Bible reproduced at least in large part for its own value. Printings of separate books of the Bible would certainly belong too, as well as the many separate editions of the New Testament.

This exhibit, then, is fairly rigorously limited to Bibles or portions of Bibles only. I have chosen particular copies to satisfy a number of purposes: to suggest indirectly some of the opportunities for Biblical or historical scholarship in the Research Center's collection; to illustrate in small part at least something of the history of the translation of the Bible; to show some fine examples of the printing of the Bible; finally, simply to show a number of Bibles that are of interest, occasionally even of amusement. I hope that even this selection will demonstrate why the American colloquial term "The Good Book" in a fine and fitting name.

Austin, September, 1960   EDWIN T. BOWDEN

PREFACE TO THE REVISED EDITION

THE IMPACT OF THE BIBLE ON civilization has indeed been vast. Not only has the Bible formed the basis for the Christian religion but it has also influenced art, literature, and even science from pre-Renaissance days down to the era of the space walk and Edward Albee. In modern times one finds an artist like Salvador Dali patterning images on Biblical events and a writer like T. S. Eliot making Biblical allusions in *The Waste Land*. These acts give us cause to turn back to the first account of creation. Bibles, then, function as one of the cornerstones of modern thought and fulfill a significant role in a research collection.

In 1960 the importance of the Bible was emphasized at the University of Texas by an exhibit of over fifty items of note. Providing points of interest and importance on each book displayed, the exhibit catalogue was a useful guide to some of the significant facets of the University of Texas collection of Bibles. The present work, an expansion of the original catalogue, has maintained an organization similar to its predecessor. The need for this expansion results from two developments. First, numerous volumes in the University of Texas Library collection were precluded from the 1960 catalogue due to limited exhibit space. (Some of the books described herein are so large and heavy that only one volume can be carried from the vault at one time). Secondly, acquisitions and gifts in the past six years have added strength to the collection.

A recent acquisition, *La Bibbia d'Este,* in facsimile, affords an exact reproduction of every detail on a unique Italian illuminated manuscript important to the history of Bible production. Most significant is the addition to the collection of the two-volume Jenson Bible of 1476. However, these are only two of many new items to be listed in the present work.

The purpose of this expansion of the 1960 catalogue is not to make a complete survey of the University of Texas Library collection of Bibles nor is it to add to the already extensive body of bibliographical and scholarly knowledge on the Bible. It is intended to enable anyone interested in Bibles to learn some useful facts about different editions and to gain some concept of the collection as it exists at the University of Texas.

Austin, February, 1967   DAVID R. FARMER

CONTENTS

IN THE BEGINNING

GOD CREATED THE HEAVEN AND THE EARTH. ⟨AND THE EARTH WAS WITHOUT FORM, AND VOID; AND DARKNESS WAS UPON THE FACE OF THE DEEP, & THE SPIRIT OF GOD MOVED UPON THE FACE OF THE WATERS. ⟨And God said, Let there be light: & there was light. And God saw the light, that it was good: & God divided the light from the darkness. And God called the light Day, and the darkness he called Night. And the evening and the morning were the first day. ⟨And God said, Let there be a firmament in the midst of the waters, & let it divide the waters from the waters. And God made the firmament, and divided the waters which were under the firmament from the waters which were above the firmament: & it was so. And God called the firmament Heaven. And the evening & the morning were the second day. ⟨And God said, Let the waters under the heaven be gathered together unto one place, and let the dry land appear: and it was so. And God called the dry land Earth; and the gathering together of the waters called he Seas: and God saw that it was good. And God said, Let the earth bring forth grass, the herb yielding seed, and the fruit tree yielding fruit after his kind, whose seed is in itself, upon the earth: & it was so. And the earth brought forth grass, & herb yielding seed after his kind, & the tree yielding fruit, whose seed was in itself, after his kind: and God saw that it was good. And the evening & the morning were the third day. ⟨And God said, Let there be lights in the firmament of the heaven to divide the day from the night; and let them be for signs, and for seasons, and for days, & years: and let them be for lights in the firmament of the heaven to give light upon the earth: & it was so. And God made two great lights; the greater light to rule the day, and the lesser light to rule the night: he made the stars also. And God set them in the firmament of the heaven to give light upon the earth, and to rule over the day and over the night, & to divide the light from the darkness: and God saw that it was good. And the evening and the morning were the fourth day. ⟨And God said, Let the waters bring forth abundantly the moving creature that hath life, and fowl that may fly above the earth in the open firmament of heaven. And God created great whales, & every living creature that moveth, which the waters brought forth abundantly, after their kind, & every winged fowl after his kind: & God saw that it was good. And God blessed them, saying, Be fruitful, & multiply, and fill the waters in the seas, and let fowl multiply in the earth. And the evening & the morning were the fifth day. ⟨And God said, Let the earth bring forth the living creature after his kind, cattle, and creeping thing, and beast of the earth after his kind: and it was so. And God made the beast of the earth after his kind, and cattle after their kind, and every thing that creepeth upon the

27

First page from THE ENGLISH BIBLE. London: The Doves Press, 1903–05. (56)

10

I

MANSCRIPTS, FACSIMILES, AND EARLY EDITIONS OF MANUSCRIPTS

1. NOVUM TESTAMENTUM GRAECUM E CODICE MS. ALEXANDRINO. . . . [ca. 440]

A facsimile in uncial character prepared by the British Museum in 1768 of the second of three great Greek codices to become known. Probably written in the first half of the fifth century, the Codex Alexandrinus contains a complete text of the Bible, including the apocrypha of the Old Testament and non-canonical writings at the end of the New Testament.

2. EVANGELIORUM QUATTUOR CODEX DURMACHENSIS. [ca. 590]

A two-volume facsimile of the Book of Durrow printed in Olten in 1960. The book acquired its name from association with the monastery of Durrow in King's County. Durrow was the center of the Columban institutions in Ireland founded by St. Columba about 553. The two subsequent centers for the movement were Iona and Kells. The original codex was once contained in a silver-mounted shrine or cumdach which has long since disappeared. The shrine was ordered by Flann, King of Ireland, between 879–916.

3. EVANGELIORUM QUATTUOR CODEX CENANNENSIS. [ca. 650]

A fine facsimile of the Book of Kells prepared in 1950 by Urs Graf-Verlag in Bern. The Book of Kells is generally considered the finest known example of the Celtic art of illumination and one of the most beautiful of all medieval books in Latin. The original manuscript, written in black, purple, red, and yellow inks, contains the four gospels, a fragment of the interpretation of Hebrew names, the Eusebian Canons, summaries of the gospels, and grants of lands to the Abby of Kells. The Book of Kells was written at Iona in honor of St. Columba and was probably brought to the mainland by Cellach, the Abbot of Iona, who was forced from the island by Norsemen between 806 and 813.

4. THE GOLDEN LATIN GOSPELS IN THE LIBRARY OF J. PIERPONT MORGAN. [ca. 695]

This facsimile, prepared in New York in 1910, is of a bicolumnar purple codex written in letters of burnished gold around the seventh or eighth century. The manuscript was formerly known as the "Hamilton Gospels" and sometimes as "King Henry the VIIIth's Gospels."

5. EVANGELIORUM QUATTUOR CODEX LINDISFARNENSIS. [ca. 700]

Urs Graf-Verlag printed this facsimile in Olten and Lausanne in 1956. It is of the early Anglo-Saxon manuscript of the Gospels known as the "Lindisfarne Gospels" or the "Durham Book" or the "Book of St. Cuthbert," probably the most beautiful specimen of Anglo-Saxon manuscript extant. These Gospels contain Jerome's Latin version with Northumbrian interlineations or glosses. The Latin text is the work of Eadfrith, Bishop of Lindisfarne (698–721); the Anglo-Saxon gloss was added later (ca. 950) by a priest named Aldred who may have been the Bishop of Durham. This is no. 49 of an edition of 680 copies.

6. THE FOUR GOSPELS. [ca. 1150]

A twelfth century manuscript of the Gospels in Greek comprised of 263 folios on parchment. This manuscript was purchased in 1893 on the Island of Prinkipo in the Sea of Marmara by Judge A. W. Terrell who presented it to the University of Texas. Listed in DeRicci and Wilson's manuscript census, Vol. 2, p. 2156.

Such manuscripts kept the Bible available to clerics, scholars, and a few wealthy men in the middle ages, and centuries later often provided useful texts for Biblical scholars.

7. THE TRINITY COLLEGE APOCALYPSE. [ca.1250]

A Roxburghe Club facsimile of the Anglo-Norman manuscript of Revelation probably produced at St. Albans or at Westminister. Three artists are believed to have been employed to create this work. One is responsible for the first sixteen leaves and the pictures of St. John's life at the end. The Trinity College Apocalypse marks the continuation of a tradition of Apocalypse pictures which began in Italy in the fourth to the sixth centuries.

inermes et sine virtute · et sine peritia
artis pugne? Vt ergo agnoscat achi-
or quoniam fallit nos · ascendamus in
montana:et cu capti fuerint potentes e-
orum tunc cu eisdem gladio transfur-
berabitur:ut sciant omnes gentes quoniam nabuchodonosor deus terre est.
et preter ipsum alius non est. Vt factum est autem cu cessassent lo-
qui:indignat' holofernes vehe-
menter dixit ad achior . Quoniam pro
phetasti nobis dicens gp gens isrl de-
fendatur a deo suo:ut ostendam tibi
quoniam non est deus nisi nabuchodo-
nosor.cu percusserim' eos omnes sicut
hominem unu:tunc et ipse cum illis assi-
riorum gladio interibis:et omnis isrl
tecu pditione dispiet:et pbabis quoniam nabuchodonosor dominus sit
uniuerse terre. Tuncp gladius milicie
mee transiet per latera tua:z cōiectus ca-
des inter uulneratos israhel:et non re-
spirabis ultra donec extermineris cu
illis. Porro aut si pphetia tuam uera
estimas non conudat uultus tuus:
et pallor qui faciem tuam obtinet absce-
dat a te:si uerba mea hec putas imple-
ri non posse . Vt aut noueris qa simul
cu illis hec experieris:ecce ex hac hora
illoru ipso sociaberis : ut dum dignas
mei gladij penas receperint:ipse simul
ultioni subiaceas. Tuc holofernes pre-
cepit seruis suis:ut comprehenderent
achior et ducerent eum in bethulia:et
traderent eum in manus filioru israhel.
Et accipientes eu serui holofernis:pro-
fecti sunt p campestria:sed cum appro-
pinquassent ad montana:egressut sut
eos fundibularij. Illi aut diuertentes
a latere mōtis:ligauerunt achior ad
arborem manibus et pedibus : et sic uinctum de restibus dimiserunt eum:z reuersi

sunt ad dominum suum. Porro filij isrl de-
scendentes de bethulia:uenerut ad eu.
Quem soluentes duxerut ad bethulia:
atcp in medium ppli illum statuerunt per-
cunctati sut · quid rerum esset cp illum
uinctum assirij reliquissent . In diebus
illis erant illic principes:ozias filius
micha de tribu symeon : et charmi qui
et gothoniel . In medio itacp seniorum
et in cōspectu oim achior dixit omnia
que locut' fuerat ab holoferne interro-
gatus : et qualiter ppls holofernis uo-
luisset ppter hoc uerbu interficere eu : et
quemadmodum ipse holofernes iratus
iusserit eum israhelitis har de causa tra-
di:ut dum uinceret filios isrl tuc et ipm
achior diuersis iuberet supplicijs interi-
re:ppter hoc cp dixisset · deus celi defen-
sor eorum est . Cumcp achior uniusa hec
exposuisset : omnis ppls cecidit in faciem
adorātes dominu:et communi lamentati-
one et fletu unanimes preces suas dno
effuderut dicentes. Domine deus celi
et terre intuere superbiam eoru z respice
ad nostra humilitatem:z facie sanctor
tuor attende:et ostende quonia non
derelinquis presumentes de te:et presumentes de se et de sua uirtute glorian-
tes humilias. Finito itacp fletu:z per
totu diem oratione ppls completa:
consolati sunt achior dicentes. Deus
patrum nostror cui' tu uirtute predi-
casti·ipse tibi hac dabit uicissitudine:
ut eor magis tu interitu uideas . Cu
uero dns deus noster dederit hanc li-
bertatem seruis suis:sit et tecum deus
in medio nostri:ut sicut placuerit tibi
ita cu tuis omnibus couerseris nobiscu.
Tunc ozias finito concilio suscepit eu
in domu suam:et fecit cenam magnam.
Et uocatis omnibus presbyteris:simul
expleto ieiunio refecerut . Postea uero

Leaf from THE GUTENBERG BIBLE. Mainz: printed before
August 24, 1456. (69)

8. THE LUTTRELL PSALTER. [ca. 1340]

A British Museum facsimile of a manuscript of the East Anglian school, written and illuminated about 1340 for Sir Geoffrey Luttrell of Irnham in Lincolnshire. Printed in London in 1932, this facsimile contains two plates in color and eighty-three in monochrome.

9. LA BIBBIA D'ESTE. 1455–1461.

The Bible of Borso d'Este printed in facsimile in Milan in 1962. There are two volumes in red morocco with gold and silver bosses on each cover. The original manuscript is an example of the finest Italian illumination and was commissioned by Borso d'Este the Magnificent to Taddeo Crivelli and Franco de Russi. The work was executed between 1455 and 1461. Movements of the two priceless original volumes throughout Europe as a result of the rise and fall of kingdoms and empires is a fascinating history in itself.

10. THE BIBLE. n.p. [ca. 1500]

An Ethiopian Bible in manuscript, this volume is bound in uncovered oak boards almost a half inch thick. The outsides of the boards have been worn smooth through use. Some chapter headings are decorated with red and black designs of interweaving lines running across the page. 147 small folio leaves.

(Williford Collection)

11. QUATTUOR D. N. JESU CHRISTI EVANGELIORUM VERSIONIS PERANTIQUAE DUAE, GOTHICA SCIL. ET ANGLO-SAXONICA. Dordrecht: H. and J. Essaeus, 1665.

The Gospels in Gothic and Anglo-Saxon from the original manuscripts. Edited by Franciscus Junius and Thomas Marshall. The first printing of the Gospels in Gothic, taken from the Codex Argenteus at the University Library in Upsala. The manuscript is of the Gothic translation by Vulfila or Ulfilas, the "Apostle of the Goths," made in the fifth or sixth century. The Anglo-Saxon text is from various manuscripts at Oxford and Cambridge.

(D&M 1604 and 4557)

et alie naues erãt cũ illo. Et facta ē p̃cella magña venti: a fluctus mittebat in nauim: ita vt impleret nauis. Et erat ipe in puppi sup ceruical dormies: et excitant eũ a dicũt illi. Magister: nõ ad te ptinet qt perimus? Et exsurges ominatus est vẽto: a dixit mari. Tace: obmutesce. Et cessauit ventus: et facta est tranquilitas magna. Et ait illis. Quid timidi estis? Necdũ habetis fidẽ? Et timuert timore magno: a dicebãt ad alterutrũ. Quis putas est iste: qt vẽtus a mare obediũt ei.

Et venerũt trãs fretum maris in regione geraseno̅. Et exeũti ei de naui statim occurrit de monumẽtis homo in spũ immũdo: qui domiciliũ habebat in monumẽtis. Et neqz cathenis iam quisqz poterat eũ ligare: qm sepe chẽ dibz a cathenis vinctus disrupissz cathenas et copedes ominuissz: a nemo poterat eum domare. Et semp die ac nocte in monumẽtis a in mõtibz erat clamans: et ocides se lapidibz. Videns aũt ihẽsuz alõge cucurrit et adorauit eũ: a clamãs voce magna dixit. Quid michi et tibi ihẽsu fili dei altissimi? Adiuro te p deum ne me torqueas. Dicebat emim illi. Exi spũs immũde ab homine isto. Et interrogabat eũ. Quod tibi nomẽ est? Et dicit ei. Legio michi nomẽ est: qt multi sumus. Et deprecabatur eũ multũ: ne se expelleret extra regione. Erat aũt ibi circa montẽ grex porco̅ magnus pascẽs in agris: Et deprecabant eũ spus dicẽtes. Mitte nos in porcos: vt in eos introeam? Et ocessit eis statim ihẽsus. Et exeũtes spũs immũdi introierũt in porcos: a magno impetu grex p̃cipitatus est in mari ad duo milia: a suffocati sũt in mari. Qui aũt pascebãt eos fugerũt: a nũciauerũt in ciuitatẽ a in agros. Et egressi sũt videre quid essz factũ: a venerũt ad ihẽsum: a vident illũ qui a demonio vexabat sedente vestitũ insane metis: et timuerũt. Et narrauerũt illis qui viderãt qualiter factũ esset ei qui demoniũ habuerat: et de porcis. Et rogare ceperũt eum: vt discederet de finibz eo̅. Cũqz ascendẽt nauim: cepit illũ deprecari q̃ a demonio vexatus fuerat vt essz cum illo: a nõ admisit euz: sz ait illi. Vade in domũ tuã ad tuos: a annũcia illis

quãta tibi dñs fecerit: et misertus sit tui. Et abijt et cepit p̃dicaẽ in decapoli: quãta sibi fecissz ihẽsus: et omes mirabãt. Et cũ ascendissz ihẽsus in nauim rursũ trãs freũ couenit turba multa ad eũ: et erat circa mare. Et venit quidaz de archisynagogis nomine iayrus: et videns eum p̃cidit ad pedes eius: et deprecabatur eũ multũ dicens: quoniã filia mea in extremis est. Veni impone manum tuã sup eã: vt salua sit et viuat. Et abijt cũ illo: et sequebatur eum turba multa: a oprimebant eũ. Et mulier q̃ erat in p̃fluuio sanguinis ãnis duodecim et fuerat multa p̃pessa a opluribz medicis: a erogauerat omnia sua. nec quicq̃ p̃fecerat: sz magis deterius habebat. Cuz audissz de ihẽsu venit in turba retro: et tetigit vestimentũ eius. Dicebat emim: qt si vel vestimẽtuz eius tetigero salua ero. Et ofestim siccatus est fons sanguinis eius: a sensit corpore: qt sanata essz a plaga. Et statim ihẽsus in semetipo ognoscens virtutẽ que exierat de illo: ouersus ad turbam aiebat. Quis tetigit vestimẽta mea? Et dicebant ei discipuli sui. Vides turbam cõprimentẽ te: a dicis quis me tetigit? Et circũspiciebat videre eã que hoc fecerat. Mulier veo timens a tremes sciens quod factũ essz in se: venit et p̃cidit ante eum et dixit ei oẽz veritatẽ. Ille aũt dixit ei. Filia fides tua te saluam fecit: vade in pace: a esto sana a plaga tua. Adhuc eo loquẽte venerũt nuntij ad archisynagogũ dicẽtes: qt filia tua mortua ē. Quid vltra vexas magistrũ? Ihẽsus aũt audito verbo quod dicebat̃ ait archisynagogo. Noli timere: tantũmodo crede. Et nõ admisit quenq̃ se sequi: nisi petrũ et iacobũ a iohannẽ fratrẽ iacobi. Et veniunt in domũ archisynagogi. Et vidit tumultum et flentes a eiulantes multũ: et ingressus ait illis. Quid turbamini et ploratis? Puella non ē mortua sz dormit. Et irridebãt eum. Ipe veo eiectis omibz assumit patrez et matrẽ puelle. et qui secũ erãt: et ingreditunt̃ vbi puella erat iacẽs: et tenẽs manũ puelle ait illi. Thabitha cumi: quod ē interpretatũ: puella tibi dico surge. Et ofestim surrexit puella: et ambulabat. Erat autez annoz duodecim. Et obstupuerũt stupore

Leaf from BIBLIA LATINA. Mainz: J. Fust and P. Schoeffer, 1462. (70)

12. HEPTATEUCHUS, LIBER JOB, ET EVANGELIUM NICODEMI; ANGLO-SAXONICE. HISTORIAE JUDITH FRAGMENTUM; DANO-SAXONICE. Oxford: The Sheldonian Theatre, 1698.

Various Anglo-Saxon fragments of the Bible edited from early manuscripts, some for the first time, by Edward Thwaites of Oxford. Another illustration of the increasing interest through the century in Biblical manuscripts of earlier tongues.

(*D&M 1606; Wing B2198*)

13. THE NEW TESTAMENT IN ENGLISH TRANSLATED BY JOHN WYCLIFFE . . . NOW FIRST PRINTED FROM A CONTEMPORARY MANUSCRIPT. Chiswick: by Charles Whittingham for William Pickering, London, 1848.

The translation by John Wycliffe and his associates, probably completed by 1382, was the first translation of the Bible into modern English. It circulated in manuscript, despite the official banning and burning that soon followed, until the appearance of the first printed Bibles. A number of Wycliffe's phrases and expressions are still familiar in modern translations.

(*Parsons copy. D&M under 1178*)

First page from BIBLIA LATINA. Venice: Nicolaus Jenson, 1476. (71)

Incipit liber genesis q dicitur hebraice bresith. Capitulum primum.

IN principio creauit deus celu z tra. Terra aut erat inanis z vacua z tenebre erat super facies abyssi: z spiritus domini ferebatur super aquas. Dixitqz deus. fiat lux. Et facta est lux. Et vidit deus lucem qz esset bona: z diuisit lucem a tenebris: appellauitqz lucem diem: z tenebras noctem. Factumqz e vespere z mane dies vnus. Dixit quoqz deus. fiat firmamentum in medio aquaz: z diuidat aquas ab aquis. Et fecit deus firmamentu. diuisitqz aquas que erant sub firmamento ab his que erant super firmamentum. Et factum est ita. Vocauitqz deus firmamentu celu. z factum est vespere z mane dies secundus. Dixit vero deus. Congregentur aque que sub celo sunt in locum vnum: z appareat arida. Et factum est ita. Et vocauit deus aridam terram: congregationesqz aquarum appellauit maria. Et vidit deus qz ect bonum: z ait. Germinet terra herbam virentem z facientem semen: z lignum pomifez faciens fructum iuxta genus suum: cuius semen i semetipso sit super terram. Et factum est ita. Et protulit terra herbam virentem z facientem semen iuxta genus suum: lignumqz faciens fructum z habens vnumquodqz sementem secundum speciem sua. Et vidit deus qz esset bonum: z factum est vespere z mane dies tertius. Dixit autem deus. fiant luminaria in firmamento celi z diuidat die ac nocte: z sint i signa z tempa

z dies z annos: ut luceat in firmamento celi: z illuminet terra. Et factum est ita. Fecitqz deus duo luminaria magna: luminare maius ut preesset diei: z luminare minus ut preesset nocti: z stellas. Et posuit eas in firmamento celi ut lucerent super terram: et preessent diei ac nocti: z diuiderent lucem ac tenebras. Et vidit deus qz esset bonum: z factu est vespere z mane dies quartus. Dixit etiam deus. Producant aque reptile anime viuentis z volatile super terra sub firmamento celi. Creauitqz deus cete grandia: z omnem animam viuentem atqz motabilem quam produxerant aque i species suas: z omne volatile secundum genus suum. Et vidit deus qz ess bonu. benedixitqz eis dicens. Crescite z multiplicamini: z replete aquas maris: auesqz multiplicentur super terram. Et factum est vespere z mane dies quitus. Dixit quoqz deus. Producat terra animam viuentem in genere suo: iumenta z reptilia: z bestias terre secundu species suas. Factumqz e ita. Et fecit deus bestias terre iuxta species suas: iumenta z omne reptile terre in genere suo. Et vidit deus qz esset bonu: z ait. Faciamus hoiem ad imaginem z similitudinem nostram: z presit piscibus maris z volatilibus celi et bestiis vniuerse terre omniqz reptili quod mouetur i terra. Et creauit deus hominem ad imaginem z similitudinem suam. ad imaginem dei creauit illum. masculum et feminam creauit eos. Benedixitqz illis deus. z ait. Crescite z multiplicamini z replete terram z subiicite eam: z dominamini piscibus maris z volatilibus celi: z vniuersis qz mouentur super terra. Dixitqz deus. Ecce dedi vobis omne herbam afferentem semen super terram z vniuersa ligna que habent in semetipsis sementem generis sui: ut sint vobis in escam: z cunctis animantibus terre: omniqz volucri celi z vniuersis que mouentur in terra z in quibus est anima viuens: ut habeant ad vescendum. Et factum est ita. Viditqz deus cuncta que fecerat: z erant valde bona. Et factu est vespere z mane dies sextus. Igitur perfecti sunt celi z terra: et omnis ornatus eorum. Compleuit qz deus die septimo opus suu qz fecerat: z requieuit die septimo ab vniuerso opere quod patrarat. Et benedixit diei

14. THE FIRST NEW TESTAMENT PRINTED IN THE ENGLISH LAN-
GUAGE (1525 or 1526), TRANSLATED FROM THE GREEK BY
WILLIAM TYNDALE; REPRODUCED IN FACSIMILE WITH AN
INTRODUCTION BY FRANCIS FRY, F.S.A.
Only 177 copies of this facsimile were issued in Bristol in
1862. Just a fragment survives today of the earliest edition
of Tyndale's translation, and it is housed in the Grenville
Collection at the British Museum.

(*D&M 1212*)

15. THE BYBLE IN ENGLYSHE, THAT IS TO SAYE THE CONTENT OF
ALL THE HOLY SCRIPTURE, BOTHE OF Y^e OLDE AND NEWE
TESTAMENT . . . London: R. Grafton and E. Whitchurch,
1539.

A fragment from the first edition of the "Great Bible," this
Bible was a revision by Coverdale of Matthew's Bible. The
printing began in Paris, but French authorities suppressed
the work at the end of 1538 and confiscated many sheets.
Coverdale and Grafton brought some sheets to London,
along with presses, type, and workmen. The edition was
completed there in April, 1539.

(*D&M 25; STC 2068*)

16. THE BYBLE IN ENGLYSHE. London: Edward Whytchurche,
1540.

(Two leaves from the 1540 Bible). The University of
Texas Library does not yet own complete examples of the
four great early English Bibles: The Tindale, the Coverdale, the Matthew or Rogers, and the Great Bible. These
leaves, however, will at least give some impression of the
Great Bible as will the fragment mentioned above. This
Bible printed in 1540 is the second edition, the first to
contain Archbishop Cranmer's prologue, and represent
Coverdale's continued revision of text and translation.

(*Parsons copy. D&M 30; STC 2070*)

Page from BIBLIA SACRA. Venice: Franciscus Renner de Heilbronn, 1482. (72)

17. **THE HOLY BIBLE**. London: R. Jugge, 1572.

The second folio edition of the Bishops' version; a remarkable feature is the Psalms in two versions printed side by side: the Prayer Book version taken from the Great Bible, in black letter type, and the Bishops' version, in Roman type.

This is sometimes called the "Leda Bible." The woodcut initial before the *Epistle to the Hebrews* was taken, as were a number of others, from an edition of Ovid's *Metamorphoses* and represents Jupiter appearing to Leda as a swan. In this copy, as so often, these amusingly inappropriate woodcuts have been partially obliterated with an ink blot by some pious former owner. With the hundreds of early settings given the Bible, it was inevitable that many misprints and typographical errors would appear. This edition contains one of the more unfortunate ones. The black letter version of *Psalms* 37:29 reads, "The righteous shall be punished." Like the Bishops' Bible of 1568, this edition contains a marginal note to Psalm 45 of particular interest to Americans: "Ophir is thought to be the Island in the west coast, of late founde by Christopher Columbo: from whence at this day is brought most fine golde."

This edition was considered an important one by the church. By order of the Convocation of Canterbury in 1571, every cathedral, and every church if possible, was to purchase a copy, and bishops were to place a copy in their "hall or large diningroom, that it might be useful to their servants or to strangers."

(*D&M 96; STC 2107*)

18. **THE BIBLE ... WITH ... ANNOTATIONS**. London: Christopher Barker, 1576.

A variant of the first edition of the Geneva Bible printed in England. The Geneva version is so called because it was translated and first published in Geneva by English non-conformist exiles, principally by William Whittingham, who based his text upon Tindale's, the Great Bible's, and Theodore Beza's Latin translation of 1557. At its appearance it was the most scholarly and critical version in English. It was the favorite version of the Puritans, English and American, and went through some 200 editions between 1560 and 1644.

(*Williford copy. D&M 107; STC 2118*)

ወእዜምር፡ ለከ፡ እምኣኪ፡ በመስዋዕ፡ ቀዲ፡ ላጅኤ፡ወ
ይታፈ፡ ሥሕ፡ ከናፍርየ፡ ዕበ፡ እዜምር፡ ለከ፡
ወበነፍ፡ ዕየ፡ እንተ፡ ፈዲ፡ ፅንከ፡
ወዓዲ፡ ልሳንየ፡ ያነብብ፡ ፅ፡ ደ፡ ቀከ፡
ሶበ፡ ተዓፋ፡ ረ፡ ወ ሐለሰ፡ ረ፡ እስ፡ የኃሠሡ፡ ፈተ፡ እኩየ

ብለ፡ኅጥ፡ ሰ ሰ፡ ሣ

ፅሙዝ፡ እ፡ ነየነ፡ ኔከ፡ ህየ፡ ልነ፡ ታ፡ ሡ
ወ ፅ፡ ደ፡ ቀ፡ ከ፡ ነ፡ ዐ ወ ል፡ ነ፡ ፤ ታ፡ ሡ
ኣ ሙ፡ ደ፡ ከ ~ ፤ ኖ ሙ፡ ሰ ሐ ዝ ብ፡ ከ፡ በ ፅ ደ ተ
ወ ል ፅ ደ ያ ፤ ገ ከ ክ፡ በ ፈ ተ ሐ
ይ ታ ወ ከ ት፡ አ ደ ባ ር ፡ ወ እ ወ ፃ ር ፡ ሰ ሙ ሐ ጎ
ከ ~ ፤ ፤ በ ደ ቅ ፤ ደ ያ ፤ ሐ ዝ በ
ወ እ ደ ስ ና ሙ ~ ሰ ደ ፅ ተ ፡ ዎ ሰ ከ ነ ፡ ዪ ከ
ወ ኤ ሰ ሠ ር ፡ ሰ ኤ በ ደ ፡ ወ ደ ጽ ነ ሀ ፡ ዎ ሰ ሰ ፡ ወ ሐ ደ
ወ ኤ ኖ ት ፅ ም ፡ ወ ር ሰ ፡ ስ ት ፡ ው ል ደ ፡ ተ ወ ል ደ
ወ ደ ወ ር ፅ ፡ ከ ም ፡ ከ ጠ ል ፡ ው ሰ ተ ፡ ኞ ም ር
ወ ኤ ም ፡ ነ ጠ ብ ጠ ብ ፡ ዛ ደ ነ ጠ ጽ ብ ፡ ደ በ ም ጽ ር
ወ ደ ሠ ር ሰ ፡ ኞ ጽ ቀ ፡ በ መ ዎ ዕ ስ ፡ ሀ
ወ በ ዙ ስ ፡ ስ ፈ ም ፡ እ ስ ከ ፡ የ ፃ ል ና ፡ ወ ር ሳ

19. THE BIBLE. TRANSLATED ACCORDING TO THE EBREW AND GREEKE, AND CONFERRED WITH THE BEST TRANSLATIONS IN DIVERS LANGUAGES. London: Christopher Barker, 1579.

This is apparently the earliest in the long series of quarto Geneva Bibles printed in England.

(*D&M 121; STC 2126*)

20. THE NEW TESTAMENT . . . TRANSLATED FAITHFULLY . . . IN THE ENGLISH COLLEGE OF RHEMES. Rhemes: John Fogny, 1582.

The first edition of the Roman Catholic version of the New Testament printed in English. It was translated by Gregory Martin from the Vulgate, and although officially condemned in England, exerted a considerable influence on the King James translation, just as Martin was influenced by the earlier English editions.

(*Parsons copy. D&M 134; STC 2884*)

21. THE BIBLE. TRANSLATED ACCORDING TO THE EBREW AND GREEKE . . . WITH MOST PROFITABLE ANNOTATIONS . . . London: Christopher Barker, 1583.

A folio black letter Geneva version. With volumes such as this one, size and weight lend much to their impressive appearance.

(*D&M 135; STC 2133*)

22. THE BIBLE TRANSLATED ACCORDING TO THE EBREW AND GREEKE . . . London: Deputies of Christopher Barker, 1588.

The Bible of Elizabeth Minshull, third wife of John Milton. Milton's signature is also pasted on the front endcover. Geneva version.

(*Parsons copy. D&M 151; STC 2148*)

23. THE TEXT OF THE NEW TESTAMENT . . . TRANSLATED . . . BY THE PAPISTS OF THE TRAITEROUS SEMINARIE AT RHEMES. WHEREUNTO IS ADDED THE TRANSLATION . . . USED IN THE CHURCH OF ENGLAND. London: Deputies of Christopher Barker, 1589.

With the Bishops' version & the Rheims New Testament in parallel columns, this was the first systematic attempt to refute the arguments and accusations contained in the

Set of illustrations from BIBLIA. Lyons: Jacobus Sacon, 1519. (75)

notes and glosses of the Roman Catholic New Testament. William Fulke the editor, Master of Pembroke College, Cambridge, alternates his refutations with the notes of Gregory Martin. Ironically, this edition secured a publicity for the Rheims version which it could not have gained by itself and increased the later influence of the Rheims version on the King James version.

(*Williford copy. D&M 156; STC 2888*)

24. THE NEW TESTAMENT. London: Deputies of Christopher Barker, 1594.

This quarto New Testament has been interleaved in a book of folio leaves on which Elizabethan notes were copiously written. The notes are in various hands, some of which are so small a magnifying glass is needed to read them comfortably. Most of the writing interprets some passage in the text. Near the end of the volume though, a number of epitaphs are written in verse. A particularly touching epitaph tells of Alexander and Juliette who died in each others arms two days after their marriage.

25. THE BIBLE . . . WITH . . . ANNOTATIONS. London: Deputies of Christopher Barker, 1597.

Bound with Sternhold and Hopkins, *The Whole Booke of Psalmes*. London, 1597.
The Geneva version with Laurence Tomson's revision of the Geneva New Testament, this was the final and popular form of the Geneva Testament. The Geneva version was the first to adopt Roman letter printing and the first English Bible to divide the chapters into verses. It is sometimes called "The Breeches Bible" because of the reading (after Wycliffe) of *Genesis* 3:7, "They sewed fig leaves together, and made themselves breeches."

(*D&M 182; STC 2168*)

26. THE NEW TESTAMENT. London: Deputies of Christopher Barker, 1598.

Bound with Sternhold and Hopkins, *The Whole Booke of Psalmes*, 1599. This little 32⁰ was bound as a decorative volume to be carried to church by a lady: calf with silver clasps and silver corners and centerpiece decorated with the Tudor rose.

(*Stark copy. D&M unlisted; STC unlisted*)

A Epitaph on Leander and
Julietta, his wife who dyed in one anothers arms
— Two days after Mariage ——

To those who death again did wed
This Tomb a second marriage Bed
For though the cruel hand of Fate
Could souls and body seperate
It could not man and wife divide
They liv'd one Life one death they dy'd
Peace, good Reader do not weep
Peace, the Lovers are asleep
They (sweet Turtles) folded lie
In the Last Knot love could tye
And, tho they lye, as they where dead
Their pillow stone, their sheets of Lead
(Pillar, hard and sheets not warm)
Love made the bed they'll take no harm
Let them sleep, let 'em sleep on
Till this stormy night be gone
And the Eternal morrow dawn
Then the curtains will be drawn
And they awake into that Light
Whose Day shall never end in night

Holograph page from THE NEW TESTAMENT. London: Deputies of Christopher Barker, 1594. (24)

27. THE BIBLE . . . WITH . . . ANNOTATIONS . . . AND . . . CON-
CORDANCE . . . London: Deputies of Christopher Barker,
1599.

A quarto black letter Geneva version which is a close reprint of the 1588 quarto.

(*D&M 187; STC 2173*)

28. THE BIBLE . . . WITH . . . ANNOTATIONS. London: Deputies
of Christopher Barker, 1599.
Bound with Sternhold and Hopkins, *The Booke of
Psalmes.* [n.p., n.d.]

The Geneva version with Tomson's revised New Testament but with the *Revelation* of Franciscus Junius, a
Huguenot divine. Despite the imprint, this Bible like
many others with the same title page was probably printed
at Amsterdam—and probably pre-dated too—for the use
of English Puritans in the Low Countries.

(*D&M 190; STC 2176*)

29. THE NEW TESTAMENT . . . SET FORTH THE SECOND TIME, BY
THE . . . COLLEGE NOW RETURNED TO DOWAY. Antwerp:
Daniel Vervliet, 1600.

The second edition of the Roman Catholic New Testament in English. This edition is historically more interesting than the first, because its notes include the answers
made to the criticisms leveled at the first edition by the
English Protestants.

(*Williford copy. D&M 198; STC 2898*)

30. THE HOLY BIBLE. London: Robert Barker, 1602.

The Bishop's Bible, a revision of the Great Bible under-
taken by Matthew Parker, Archbishop of Canterbury, with
the assistance of a number of bishops and Biblical scholars.
First published in 1568. This folio edition of 1602 was
used by the King James translators as the basis of their
new version of 1611.

The Bishops' version, like the earlier Coverdale, is sometimes called the "treacle Bible" from the reading of *Jere-
miah* 8:22, "Is there not Triacle at Gilead? Is there no
Physicion there?"

(*Woodward-Ruth copy. D&M 206 [2nd t.p.]; STC 2188*)

Title-page from THE NEW TESTAMENT. London: Deputies of
Christopher Barker, 1594. (24)

31. THE BIBLE . . . WITH . . . ANNOTATIONS . . . London: Robert Barker, 1608.

Another quarto black letter Geneva version.

(*D&M 225; STC 2203*)

32. THE HOLY BIBLE FAITHFULLY TRANSLATED . . . BY THE ENGLISH COLLEGE OF DOWAY. 2 vols. Vol. 1: Doway: Laurence Kellam, 1609. Vol. 2: [Rouen]: John Cousturier, 1635.

The first edition (1609) of the Roman Catholic version of the Old Testament in English. With the Rheims edition of 1582 it makes a complete Bible, generally called the Douai version. The work primarily of Gregory Martin too, it was translated from the Vulgate at the same time as the New Testament, and in the same literal, latinate fashion, but publication was delayed, according to the Preface, by "our poore estate in banishment." This set was made up from the first edition of volume 1 and the second edition of volume 2 by some owner of the time who had the two volumes bound in matching seventeenth century calf, not worrying in the least about bibliographical consistency.

(*D&M 231 and 387; STC 2207 and 2321*)

33. THE HOLY BIBLE . . . NEWLY TRANSLATED. London: Robert Barker, 1611.

The "King James" or "authorized" version of 1611, the text that was to remain the popular standard for over three hundred years and exert such an enormous influence on the English language and its literature. The translation is the work of fifty-four men appointed by King James after conference with the Anglican and the Puritan church. They based their text on the Bishops' Bible, but made use of all available versions. Their work has long been considered one of the great monuments of English scholarship.

The Great "He" Bible; so-called because of the reading of *Ruth* 3:15, "and *he* went into the citie." It is generally considered the first issue of the first edition. This copy has W. E. Smith's "A" readings throughout; that is, each leaf is from the first printing as far as bibliography has determined.

(*Woodward-Ruth copy. D&M 240; STC 2216*)

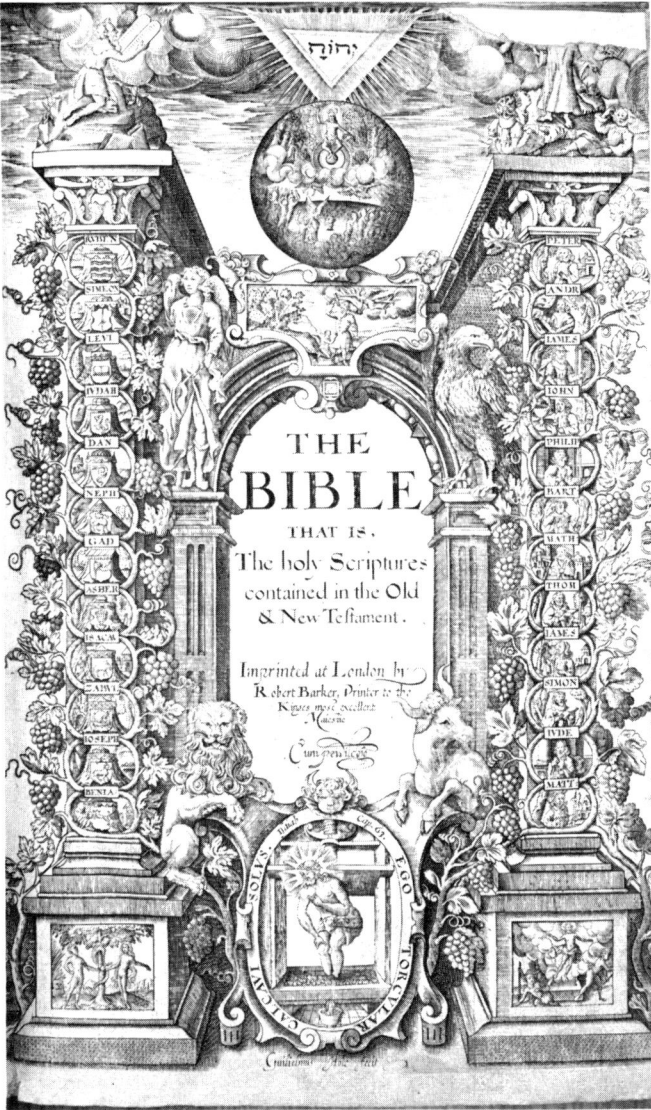

Title-page from THE HOLY BIBLE. London: Robert Barker, 1602.
(30)

34. THE HOLY BIBLE . . . NEWLY TRANSLATED. London: Robert Barker, 1611.

The Great "She" Bible; from the variant reading in *Ruth*, one of the many small differences in text and printing that distinguish what is apparently the second issue. This copy has mixed leaves of Smith's "B" and "C" readings.
(Williford copy. D&M 246; STC 2217)

35. THE HOLY BIBLE. Cambridge: Tho. and John Buck, 1629. Bound with *The Book of Common Prayer*, Cambridge, 1629 and Sternhold and Hopkins, *The Whole Book of Psalmes*, Cambridge, 1629.

The first edition of the King James version printed at Cambridge, and the first revised text of the version. The corrections in text by the Bucks seem to have been unofficial but are careful and thorough.
(D&M 324; STC 2285)

36. THE HOLY BIBLE. Cambridge: Tho. and John Buck, 1630.

This black letter volume along with D&M 331 was the first quarto edition of the King James version printed at Cambridge. The Bucks, jointly, issued only four editions— one foloio, one quarto in ordinary Roman type, and two black letter issues dated 1630 and 1633.
(D&M 332; STC 2294)

37. THE HOLY BIBLE CONTEYNING THE OLD TESTAMENT AND THE NEW. London: Barker and Assigns of Bill, 1632.

Probably published early in 1633, many copies of this edition have the figure "2" in the date changed by pen to read "3" as does this copy.
(D&M 359; STC 2303)

38. THE TEXT OF THE NEW TESTAMENT . . . TRANSLATED BY THE PAPISTS . . . AT RHEMES. London, 1633.

A fourth edition of William Fulke's work first printed in 1589.
(D&M 371; STC 2947)

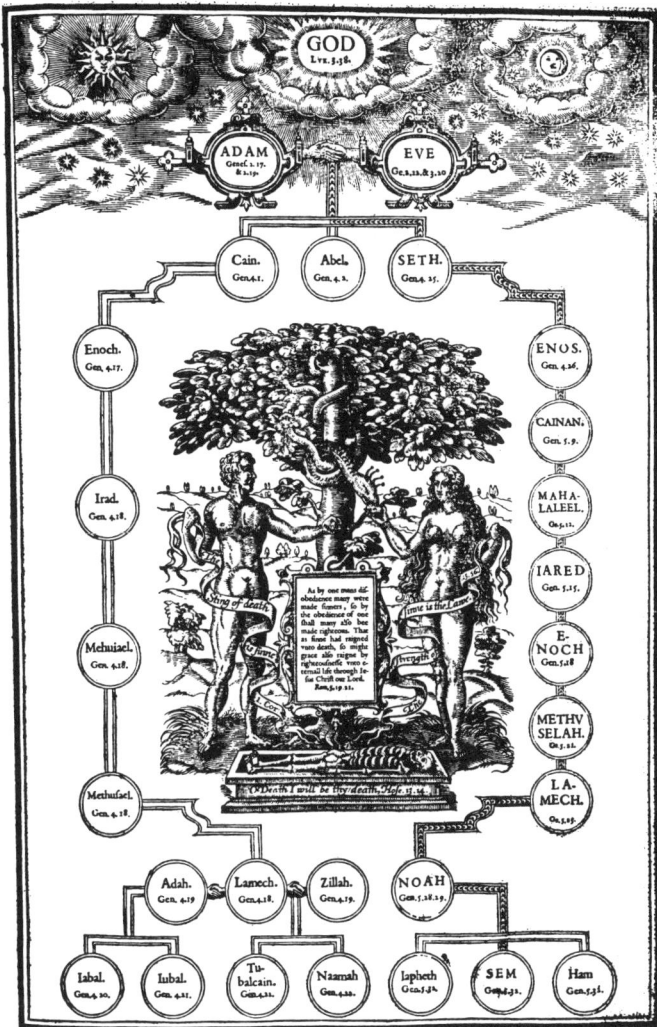

Genealogy page from the KING JAMES BIBLE. London: Robert
Barker, 1611. (33)

39. THE BAY PSALM BOOK, A FACSIMILE REPRINT OF THE FIRST
EDITION OF 1640. Chicago, 1956.

In his *American Bibliography* (Chicago, 1909), Evans
notes the *Bay Psalm Book* as the earliest printed work in
the United States of American known to be extant. Translation from Hebrew was begun in 1636 and was mainly
carried on by the Rev. Thomas Welde, the Rev. John Eliot,
and the Rev. Richard Mather, who wrote the preface.

(*Evans 4*)

40. THE HOLY BIBLE. London: John Field, 1653.

Another edition full of misprints, sometimes called "the
unrighteous Bible." 1 *Corinthians* 6:9 omits a "not" and
reads, "Know ye not that the unrighteous shall inherit the
kingdom of God?" And *Romans* 6:13 omits a similar nega-
tive "un-" and reads, "Neither yield ye your members as
instruments of righteousness unto sin."

(*Williford copy. D&M 496; Wing B2238*)

41. THE HOLY BIBLE . . . London: Bill and Executrix of New-
comb, 1702.

Lee mentions in *Memorial for the Bible Societies in Scot-
land* (Edinburgh, 1824), that many copies of this edition
were sent to the libraries established in the Highlands
early in the eighteenth century.

(*D&M 679*)

42. THE HOLY BIBLE. Cambridge: John Baskerville, 1763.

A tall folio generally considered the most magnificent
printing of John Baskerville, one of the great printers of
the century who set a new standard for design and appearance of the printed book.

(*Parsons copy. D&M 857*)

43. THE HOLY BIBLE. Oxford: T. Wright and Gill, 1776.

The Bible of Stephen Austin, brother of Moses Austin and
uncle of Stephen F. Austin, one of the families so important
to the history of early Texas.

(*Texas Archives copy*)

SACRA
BIBLIA,

Das ist

Die gantze H. Schrifft/Alten vnd Newen Testaments/nach der letzten Römischen Sixtiner Edition/ auß befehl des

Hochwürdigsten/Durchleuchtigsten Fürsten vnd Herren/Herren Ferdinanden /Ertzbischoffen zu Cöln vnd Churfürsten/rc. mit fleiß vbergesetzt/

Durch

Den Ehrwürdigen vnd Hoch gelehrten Herren CASPARVM VLENBERGIVM Lippiensem, der H. Schrifft licentiaten/Pastorn zu S. Columben in Cöln/auch vbersehen durch

Die insonder hierzu verordnete der H. Schrifft Doctorn/in der wolberümpten Vniuersitet daselbst.

Getruckt in Schleinder Lucunerlerey/

Durch Johannem Kreps.

Im Jar M. DC. XXX.

1630

Title-page from BIBLIA. Strassburg: L. Erben, 1630. (87.)

44. THE BIBLE IN MINATURE, OR A CONCISE HISTORY OF THE OLD AND NEW TESTAMENTS. London: E. Newbery, 1780. [1⅝ × 1⅛ in.]

Such Bibles were produced as curiosities and collector's pieces; some of the smaller ones cannot be read without a jeweler's glass. It is difficult to believe now that even the children's Bibles could have been intended for use, although apparently they were. For other examples see items 53, 55, 66, and 114.

45. THE HOLY BIBLE, ORNAMENTED WITH ENGRAVINGS BY JAMES FITTLER . . . London: T. Bensley, for R. Bowyer and J. Fittler, 1795.

The engravings are after pictures by Durer, Rembrandt, and Rubens, among others. This Bible belonged to Henry Charles Angelo, the eldest son of Domenico Tremamondo, the fencing master. Angelo also became a master at fencing and taught many titled pupils in his *academie*. He was close to Sheridan and Fox who used to drop in at Angelo's school for visits.

(*D&M 961*)

46. THE HOLY BIBLE CONTAINING THE OLD AND NEW TESTAMENTS, TOGETHER WITH THE APOCRYPHA . . . Worcester, Massachusetts. 1802.

The second Worcester edition by Isaiah Thomas who published his first edition in 1791. It was said of his 1791 edition that it was far ahead of any other publication in America in relation to typography, excellence of paper, and binding. Benjamin Franklin, an expert printer himself, spoke of Thomas as "the Baskerville of America."

47. THE HOLY BIBLE. 6 vols. London: Thomas Bensley, for Thomas Macklin, 1800. THE APOCRYPHA. London: T. Bensley, for T. Cadell and W. Davies, 1816.

Generally known as Macklin's Embellished Bible. A sumptuous edition to begin with, in large type with many engravings, this copy has been extended to 31 volumes with 5880 illustrations of various sorts: etchings, engravings, prints, title pages and leaves from old Bibles, and 786 original drawings and sketches. Many of the engravings are of interest, but the greatest interest is in the originals.

Binding on THE NEW TESTAMENT GOSPELS. Moscow, [ca. 1648].
(88)

Some 300 of them form the original Dandini collection of drawings, gathered at Florence by the Dandini family of artists at the end of the sixteenth and beginning of the seventeenth centuries. It is made up for the most part of drawings, sketches, and studies by the Dandinis themselves: Caesar, Vincentio, Pietro, and Ottavo Dandini. But it also contains a few examples by many of their compeers. Historically, the collection had remained together until 1858 when it was purchased by John Gray Bell of Manchester. In addition to the Dandini collection, the volumes contain more than twice that number of originals by other artists. Many of them are anonymous or attributed to minor masters, and a few are attributed to the great masters: Rubens, Veronese, Dürer, Breughel, Raphael, Rembrandt, Titian, Perugino, Andrea del Sarto, and Vandyke. Notes and bookplates show that the volumes must have been made up between 1858 and 1862, and at some time belonged to Thomas Brooke, F.S.A. before passing to the Parsons Library.

(Parsons copy. D&M 982 and 1065)

48. THE HOLY BIBLE . . . WITH ILLUSTRATIONS BY GUSTAVE DORÉ. 2 vols. London and New York: Cassell, Petter, and Galpin, [n.d.]

Another extended Bible, this one enlarged from 2 to 20 volumes by the addition of some 4500 engravings, etchings, prints, woodcuts, title pages and specimen pages, and a number of original drawings, the majority by Richard Westall (1765–1836) of the Royal Academy. Many of the woodcuts and etchings are early and apparently original ones, the most notable being a small number by Dürer and Rembrandt. New title pages were especially printed for each volume.

(Parsons copy. D&M unlisted)

49. ILLUSTRATIONS OF THE BOOK OF JOB BY WILLIAM BLAKE. London, 1826.

Blake was interested in the theme and misfortunes of Job since 1793 and produced here a collection of 21 engravings on the subject. The illustration used from this volume pictures the Behemoth and the Leviathan. They were the creatures of the natural world representing the powers of the earth and sea.

Title-page from BIBLIA SACRA POLYGLOTTA. London: Thomas Roycroft, 1655. (90)

50. THE HOLY BIBLE, CONTAINING THE OLD AND NEW TESTA-
MENTS. Oxford: S. Collingwood and Company, 1839.

This Bible was in the Coleridge family and records the date and exact minute of the death of Samuel Taylor Coleridge's eldest son, Hartley, and his only daughter, Sara. Hartley died on Thursday, January 6, 1849 "at ten minutes to 1 P.M.." and Sara died on Monday, May 3, 1852 "at 5 o'clock P.M."

(D&M 1156)

51. THE BIBLE. Edinburgh: Cowand and Company, 1856.

The Bible of Robert Louis Stevenson. It originally belonged to his father, Thomas Stevenson, who made many manuscript notes on interleaved pages.

(Stark copy. D&M unlisted)

52. THE HOLY BIBLE . . . New York: American Bible Society, 1860.

The Bible of James S. Hogg, the governor of Texas, 1891–95, an important figure in the history of modern Texas.

(Texas Archives copy.)

53. THE NEW TESTAMENT. Glascow: University Press for David Bryce and Son, 1895. [¾ ×⅝ in.]

54. THE BIBLE. Springfield: W. J. Holland, n.d.

This illustrated edition of the Bible is from the collection of Edgar Lee Masters.

(Academic Center copy.)

55. THE NEW TESTAMENT ("The Finger New Testament"). Oxford: The University Press, [n.d.]. [3½ × 1].

56. THE ENGLISH BIBLE. 5 vols. London: The Doves Press, 1903–05.

Ruari McLean speaks of the Doves Press Bible as the greatest book of the Press, "one of the noblest printed

806 DEUTERONOMIUM. CAP. XXII.

Versio VULG. LAT.

3 Similiter facies de asino, & de
vestimento, & de omni re
fratris tui, quæ perierit: si
inveneris eam, ne negligas
4 quasi alienam. Si videris
asinum fratris tui aut bovem
cecidisse in via, non despi-
cies, sed sublevabis cum eo.
5 Non induetur mulier veste
virili, nec vir utetur veste
fœmineâ: abominabilis enim
apud Deum est, qui facit
6 hæc. Si ambulans per viam,
in arbore vel in terra nidum avis inveneris, & ma-
trem pullis vel ovis de-
super incubantem; non te-
7 nebis eam cum filiis: Sed
abire patieris, captos tenens
filios: ut benè sit tibi, &
8 longo vivas tempore. Cùm
ædificaveris domum novam,
facies murum tecti per circui-
tum: ne effundatur sanguis
in domo tua, & sis reus la-
bente alio, & in præceps
9 ruente. Non seres vineam
tuam altero semine: ne & se-
mentis quam sevisti, & quæ
nascuntur ex vinea, pariter
10 sanctificentur. Non arabis in
11 bove simul & asino. Non in-
duéris vestimento, quod ex
lana linóque contextum est.
12 Funiculos in fimbriis facies
per quatuor angulos pallii
13 tui, quo operiéris. Si duxerit
vir uxorem, & posteà odio
14 habuerit eam, Quæsieritque
occasiones quibus dimittat
eam, objiciens ei nomen pes-
simum, & dixerit; Uxorem
hanc accepi, & ingressus ad
eam non inveni virginem:
15 Tollent eam pater & mater
ejus, & ferent secum signa virginitatis ejus ad seniores ur-
16 bis qui in porta sunt. Et di-
cet pater, Filiam meam dedi huic uxorem: quam quia
odit,

Versio GRÆCA LXX. Interp. Cum Translatione LATINA.

Versio SYRIACA cum Interpretatione LATINA.

Idem fac tauro, & asino ejus, & vesti- 3
mento ipsius: idemque fac cuicunque rei
amissæ quæ perierit ab eo, & quam repe-
reris: non enim licet tibi dissimulare.
Non videbis asinum inimici tui aut bovem 4
succumbentes in via, & negliges eos: sed
erigendo erige eos cum illo. Ne sint ve- 5
stes viriles super mulierem, nec induatur vir
vestimentis muliebribus, quoniam abomi-
nandus est coram Domino Deo tuo qui-
cunque talia fecerit. Et cùm inveneris 6
nidum avis ante te in via in quacunque arbore aut super terram, pullos *videlicet*, aut
ova, & matrem incubantem pullis aut
ovis, ne capias matrem cum pullis suis:
Sed avolare fac matrem, pullos autem ejus 7.
sume tibi, ut bene tibi sit, & multiplicentur dies tui. Et quando extrues domum 8
novam, fac balaustium tecto tuo, ne cadat
ex eo aliquis, & sit sanguis in domo tua.
Ne seras arvum tuum miscellaneis, ne san- 9
ctificetur proventus seminis quod seres, &
proventus vineæ. Ne ducas aratrum cum 10
tauro & cum asino simul. Ne induas varia 11
ex lana & lino simul. Intextas fimbrias fac 12
tibi in quatuor marginibus pallii tui quo
operiris. Et cùm duxerit quispiam uxorem, 13
& ingressus fuerit ad eam, & oderit eâ, Tra- 14
xeritque post eam occasionem in verbis, &
promulgaverit de ea nomen malum, ac dixerit, Uxorem hanc duxi, & dormivi apud
eam, nec inveni ei virginitatem; Tollet 15
pater puellæ & mater ejus, & proferent
signa virginitatis puellæ ad seniores civita-
tis, ad portam. Dicetque pater puellæ 16
senioribus, Filiam meam dedi viro isti
uxorem, estque eam odio prosequutus.

Page from BIBLIA SACRA POLYGLOTTA. London: Thomas Roycroft, 1655. (90)

books ever made." Holbrook Jackson said of it "there is nothing, for instance, quite so effective as the first page of the Doves Bible, with its great red initial 'I' dominating the left-hand margin of the opening chapter of Genesis like a symbol of the eternal wisdom and simplicity of the wonderful Book. Neither foliation nor arabesque could better have introduced the first verse of the Creation than this flaming, sword-like initial. This edition of the Bible in itself represents the last refuge of the complex in the simple. . . ."

(Parsons copy)

57. THE HOLY BIBLE. Philadelphia: 1914.

This copy of the Bible was presented to J. Frank Dobie with the following inscription: "Compliments of the Women's Christian Temperance Union of Beeville, Texas."

(J. Frank Dobie Collection)

58. GENESIS. The First Chapter. London: The Nonesuch Press, 1924.

One of the early Nonesuch Press books, this edition of the first chapter of Genesis has twelve woodcuts by Paul Nash. It was printed on Zanders hand-made paper in an edition of 375 copies of which this is No. 348.

(Book Arts Collection)

59. THE HOLY BIBLE . . . ACCORDING TO THE AUTHORIZED VERSION. 5 vols. London: The Nonesuch Press, 1924–27.

Ruari McLean in *Modern Book Design,* (London, 1958), notes that the Nonesuch Press was founded "with the aim of producing fine editions by modern methods, and actually for reading, not as ornaments." Francis Meynell, the founder, was not limited by his own equipment, but would go anywhere for type, paper, and the technique which would produce the effect he desired.

This edition of the Bible is one of 1000 copies on Japon vellum with typography and design by Meynell and copper-plate engravings by Stephen Godden. Copies are to be found in the Parsons Collection as well as the Alfred Knopf Collection.

Title-page from THE GOSPELS IN GOTHIC. Dordrechti, 1665.
(92)

60. THE FOUR GOSPELS OF THE LORD JESUS CHRIST. Waltham St. Lawrence at Birkshire: The Golden Cockerel Press, 1931.

A handsomely produced book of the Gospels with type and engraved decorations by Eric Gill. At the beginning of many chapters the artist has interrelated figures with capital letters and even with entire words.

(*Book Arts Collection*)

61. THE HOLY BIBLE CONTAINING THE OLD AND NEW TESTAMENTS . . . Oxford, 1935.

The "Lectern Bible" designed by Bruce Rogers. Still another example of the attention given to fine printing in modern times.

62. THE SONG OF SONGS. Waltham St. Lawrence at Birkshire: The Golden Cockerel Press, 1936.

In the Latin Bible (the Vulgate) the title of this book is *Canticum canticorum Salomonis* while the *Septuagint* names it the "Song of Songs, which is Solomon's." The Hebrew text goes back to Ben Chayyim's "Massoretic" text which was traditionally read in the Synagogue. Scholars believe this text was constructed no earlier than the fifth century. The earliest known manuscript belongs to the ninth century. Some elements of the *Song of Songs*, though, go back as far as 1000 B.C.

This Golden Cockerel Press edition has copper engravings by Lettice Sandford. 204 copies were printed of which numbers 5–69 were specially bound and accompanied by six additional plates. No. 33.

(*Book Arts Collection*)

63. THE HOLY BIBLE. Cleveland and New York: The World Publishing Company, 1949.

One of 975 copies. An extremely large volume (17¼ × 14½ in.) with attractive and readable typography. This edition was designed by Bruce Rogers and illustrates the attractive work that can be done by large commercial presses rather than by the private presses that are so often thought of as the only creators of fine printing. There are copies in the Stark and Knopf collections.

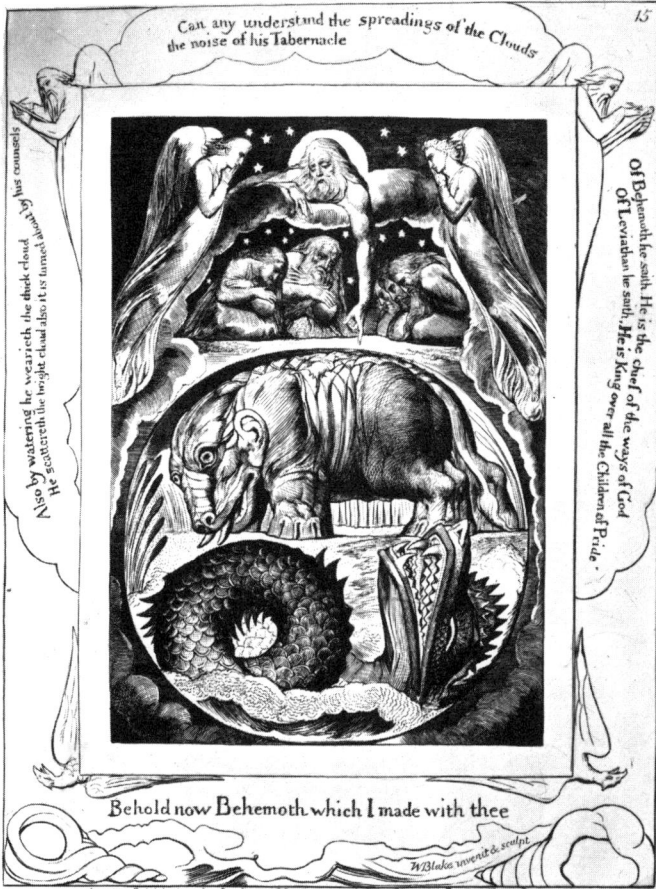

Plate #15 from ILLUSTRATIONS OF THE BOOK OF JOB BY WILLIAM BLAKE. London, 1826. (49)

64. THE HOLY BIBLE. Oxford: The Oxford University Press, n.d.

The Bible of D. H. Lawrence initialed "D.H.L." on the free front end-paper and signed "D.H. Lawrence" on the title-page.

(*Academic Center copy.*)

65. THE HOLY BIBLE. London: Eyre and Spottiswoode, Ltd., n.d.

Edith Sitwell's Bible in which she listed certain pages and marked passages which were important to her.

(*Academic Center copy.*)

66. THE LORD'S PRAYER. Munich, c. 1952. [¼ × ¼ in.]

An infinitesimal polyglot in seven languages, cased in its own jewel box.

67. BIBELIN MED BILDER AV REMBRANDT. Stockholm: 1954.

This is the first complete publication of the Bible with pictures by Rembrandt. All other Rembrandt Bibles before this printed only the text which referred to the reproduced pictures of the artist. The Stockholm Rembrandt Bible contains the unabridged text of the Old and the New Testament as well as the Apocrypha. Rembrandt was never commissioned by any publisher to supply a uniform series of Bible illustrations; however, he always chose for his work subjects which appealed most strongly to him.

68. THE PASSION ACCORDING TO SAINT MATTHEW. Marazion Cornwall: The Ark Press, 1954.

The first publication of The Ark Press, this volume contains the text of the Passion of St. Matthew cut in linoleum by John Cossar and five illustrations by Ru Van Rossem. The full-page illustrations combine three media: deep etching, copper engraving, and acquatint. A different color range is employed in each plate.

Each page of text is cut on a separate block of linoleum: a modern undertaking in the manner of the block books that pre-dated the era of moveable type. No. 4 of 25 copies.

(*Book Arts Center Collection*)

Map from THE HOLY BIBLE. London and New York: Cassell, Petter, and Galpin, n.d. (48)

III
NOTABLE EDITIONS IN LANGUAGES
OTHER THAN ENGLISH

69. THE GUTENBERG BIBLE. Mainz: printed before August 24, 1456.

A vellum facsimile reproduced from the copies in the Konigliche Bibliothek, Berlin, and the Standische Landesbibliothek in Fulda. 300 copies were produced; however, this is no. 1 of three copies on vellum. The three special copies were illuminated by Ansgar Schoppmeyer.

The Gutenberg Bible is also known as the "Mazarine Bible" or the "42-line Bible." The original is generally considered both the first Bible and the first large book printed in Europe with movable type. It has long been attributed to Johann Gutenberg, although scholars are now suggesting that it may have been primarily the work of Johann Fust, a patron of Gutenberg and successor to his establishment when the printer went bankrupt in 1455. The text is that of Jerome's Vulgate.

The University of Texas Library also has 2 leaves of the original which contains parts of Chapter VII, all of Chapter VIII, and parts of Chapter IX of Leviticus and Chapters VI and VII of Judith. Both leaves are rubricated.

70. BIBLIA LATINA. Mainz: J. Fust and P. Schoeffer, 1462.

A fragment containing parts of Chapter III, all of Chapter IV, and parts of Chapter V of Mark. Fust and Schoeffer's was the earliest edition of the Bible to bear the name of a printer and a date of publication, (August 14, 1462). This edition also is the first instance of a book formally divided into two volumes. *The Historical Catalogue of Printed Bibles,* (London, 1903), provides an interesting note which sheds light on some approaches to printing in its early days: "According to a familiar story, many copies of this edition were sold in Paris as manuscripts for 60 crowns apiece, and, from their number and the extraordinary resemblance between them, they were supposed to have been executed by magic. Some colour is given to this story by the variations in the colophon, one form omitting all allusion to the art of printing, and another explicitly referring to the mechanical process."

(D&M 6080; Hain 3050; Goff B-529)

Illustration of Jerusalem from THE HOLY BIBLE. London and
New York: Cassell, Petter, and Galpin, n.d. (48)

71. BIBLIA LATINA. Venice: Nicolaus Jenson, 1476. 2 vols.

The earliest edition of the Bible printed by Nicolaus Jenson in Venice. The copy in the Stark Library is printed on the finest quality vellum and has numerous illuminations, the most magnificent of which is the first page of *Genesis*. The gold leaf as well as the colors used on this first illustrated page are still as brilliant as they were almost five hundred years ago. Only two copies on vellum have been recorded in America. Bound in French eighteenth century red morocco.

(D&M under 6081; Hain 3061; Goff B-547)

72. BIBLIA SACRA, CUM POSTILLIS NICOLAI DE LYRA. 2 vols. Venice: Franciscus Renner de Heilbronn, [1482–83].

A fine example of fifteenth century Venetian printing and illumination. The commentary by Nicholas de Lyra was the beginning of printed exegesis, and is generally considered to have influenced Luther, and so to have helped to lead to the Reformation. Latin Vulgate version.

(Parsons copy. D&M 6080; Goff B-612)

73. BIBLIA. Venice: Hieronymus de Paganinis Brixiensis, 1492.

The second octavo edition of the Bible in Latin and is dated September 7, 1492. This Bible and the folio edition printed by Brixiensis in the same year are the first to have a woodcut on the title page. Precise dating such as in this edition is not uncommon in items of incunabula.

(D&M 6087; Hain 3114; Goff B-594)

74. SACRAE SCRIPTURAE VETERIS, NOVAEQUE OMNIA. Venice: The Aldine Press, 1518.

This is the first edition of the complete Bible in Greek apart from the Complutensian Polyglot that had already been printed but not yet circulated. It was edited by Andreas Asolanus, father-in-law of Aldus Manutius the printer. The text was apparently derived from several Greek manuscripts belonging to Cardinal Bessarion.

(Parsons copy. D&M 4594)

Ps. l. 19.
Tunc acceptabis sacrificium iusticie, obla,
ciones et holocausta: tunc imponent super
altare tuum vitulos.

ÞAN schalt thu sacrifice accepte,
Of rightfulnes and treuthe entyer,
And calveren after thi recepte,
Schul men leyen on thin autyer.
On calverie a calf ther crepte,
Crist on croys bothe clene and cleer,
For teris that his moder wepte,
He schilde us from the fendis feer.

Ps. ci. 1.
Domine exaudi oracionem meam: et clamor
meus ad te veniat.

LORD thu herkyn my prayere,
And to the lat com my cry,
Vouchesaf to lysten & here,
The mone that y make mekely.
To crie on the with carful
chere,
That nedith no man so mychel as y,
Therfor my stevene strengthe and stere,
That y not speke unspedely.

THE

NEW TESTAMENT

OF

OUR LORD AND SAVIOUR JESUS CHRIST,

TRANSLATED INTO

THE CHOCTAW LANGUAGE.

———————

PIN

CHITOKAKA PI OKCHALINCHI CHIS*v*S KLAIST

IN TESTAMENT HIMONA,

CHAHTA ANUMPA ATOSHOWA HOKE.

———————

NEW YORK:

AMERICAN BIBLE SOCIETY,

INSTITUTED IN THE YEAR MDCCCXVI.

———

1854.

Title-page from THE NEW TESTAMENT TRANSLATED INTO THE CHOCTAW LANGUAGE. New York: American Bible Society, 1854. (106)

50

75. BIBLIA. Lyons: Jacobus Sacon, 1519.

One of the several editions issued by Jacques Sacon for A. Koburger of Nuremburg between 1506 and 1522. Sacon is known to have reprinted the best contemporary editions. This edition has numerous woodcuts by Hans Springinklee.

(*D&M 6091*)

76. NOVUM TESTAMENTUM . . . AB ERASMO ROTERODAMO RECOGNITUM. Basel: Johanus Frobenius, 1522.

The third edition of Desiderius Erasmus' Greek text of the New Testament. The text was not particularly accurate, but at its first appearance in 1516 was the only printed one available and so exercised a great influence on later editions.

(*D&M 4599*)

77. BIBLIA VTRIVSQUE TESTAMENTI IVSTA VVLAGATAM TRANSLATEONEM & EAM QUAM HABERI POTUIT EMENDATISSIMAM: CUI IN NOUO, APOSUIMUS DES. ERASMI ROT . . . Basel: Froben, March 1538.

This folio edition prints Erasmus' version side by side with the Vulgate in the New Testament.

(*D&M under 6115; Copinger 261*)

78. THE PENTATEUCH. Paris: Stephanus, 1543.

The books of Genesis, Exodus, Leviticus, Numbers, and Deuteronomy printed in Hebrew. Robertus Stephanus was responsible for many of the Bibles in Hebrew and was later persecuted for making Bibles available to lay people.

(*Hebraica-Judaica collection*)

79. BIBLIA. Bound in 2 vols. Paris: Robertus Stephanus, 1545.

One of the many editions of Robertus Stephanus (or Estienne or Etienne), the eminent French printer and scholar whose Biblical work was so influential on later texts. His text was to become the foundation of the official Roman Vulgate. In this edition the Vulgate is printed in parallel columns with the Zurich version, a Latin translation from the Hebrew of the Jewish canonical books first published two years before.

(*D&M 6127*)

80. HEBRAICUS PENTATEUCHUS LATINUS PLANEQUE NOUUS POST OMNES HOCTENUS AEDITIONES EUULAGATUS AC HEBRAICAE VERITATI . . , CONFORMATUS. Venice: 1551.

An edition of the Pentateuch and the Megilloth in Hebrew and Latin with Latin notes drawn from Rabbinical sources. This edition was prepared by Sebastian Munster, (1489–1552), a German Hebraist and geographer as well as a Protestant scholar. He taught Hebrew at the University of Basel in 1529 and studied under Elijh Levita (Elyahu Bahur) whose grammatical works he edited and translated.

(*Hebraica-Judaica collection*)

81. BIBLIA SACRA. Lyons: Johannus Tornaesius, 1554.

Another set of interesting woodcuts. This is said to be the earliest edition to contain the illustrations of Bernard Salomon, generally called "le petit Bernard."

(*Parsons copy. D&M note after 6134*)

82. BIBLIA, AD VETUSTISSIMA EXEMPLARIA CASTIGATA. Antwerp: Christopher Plantin, 1565.

In 1559 was printed the first edition of the Latin Bible published by Christopher Plantin, the master printer in Antwerp. This is a reprint by Plantin of his 1559 Louvain Bible.

(*DeGolyer Collection*)

83. LA BIBLIA . . . TRASLADADA EN ESPANOL. [Basel: Thomas Guarinus], 1569.

The first edition of the complete Bible in Spanish, it was translated by Cassiodoro de Reina, one of the Spanish Reformers in exile. His version of the Old Testament is based on the Hebrew, and the New Testament on the Greek. Although 2600 copies were printed, the edition is said to have been very scarce when a revision was published in Amsterdam in 1602.

(*D&M 8472*)

84. IESU CHRISTI, D.N. NOUU TESTAMENTU, GR. & LAT. THEODORO BEZA INTERPRETE . . . Geneva: H. Estienne, 1590.

This is the third minor edition of the text translated by

Binding on THE ENGLISH BIBLE. London: The Doves Press, 1903–05. (56)

Theodoro Beza (1519–1605), a Reformation scholar who became Calvin's coadjutor and successor at Geneva.

(D&M under 4651)

85. BIBLIA HEBRAICA. Geneva, 1609.

A reprint of the Antwerp 1584 Bible in the original languages with an interlinear Latin translation. The 1584 edition was a reprint of the Antwerp Polyglot, D&M 1422.

(D&M 5113)

86. NOVUM TESTAMENTUM GRAECUM, CUM VULGATA INTERPRETATIONE LATINA GRAECI CONTEXTUS LINEIS INSERTA . . . Geneva, 1609.

A reprint of Plantin's 1584 edition.

(D&M 4662)

87. BIBLIA . . . VERTEUTSCHT: DURCH D. MARTIN LUTHER. Strassburg: Lazari Zetzners Seligen Erben, 1630.

One of the later folio editions of Luther's version.

(D&M 4217)

88. THE NEW TESTAMENT GOSPELS [in Church Slavonic]. Moscow: circa 1648.

An elaborate, three dimensional binding of gold-dipped silver over oak boards. The front cover is of five separate panels with bas-relief sculptures of Matthew, Mark, Luke and John surrounding the crucifixion. The spine is decorated with angels and flowers in heavy bas-relief, and the back cover, in one piece with decorated, raised corners to protect the central sculpture, shows a rather Slavic Jerusalem and the empty cross. The detail of the sculpture is fine and sharp.

(Parsons copy)

89. VETUS TESTAMENTUM GRAECUM EX VERSIONE SEPTUAGINTA INTERPRETUM, JUXTA EXEMPLAR VATICANUM ROMAE EDITUM . . . London: R. Daniel, 1653.

This is the first edition of the Septuagint printed in England. It was edited by John Biddle (1615–1662), a controversial Unitarian who was imprisoned for his religious views by the Parliamentary Commissioners.

(D&M 4692)

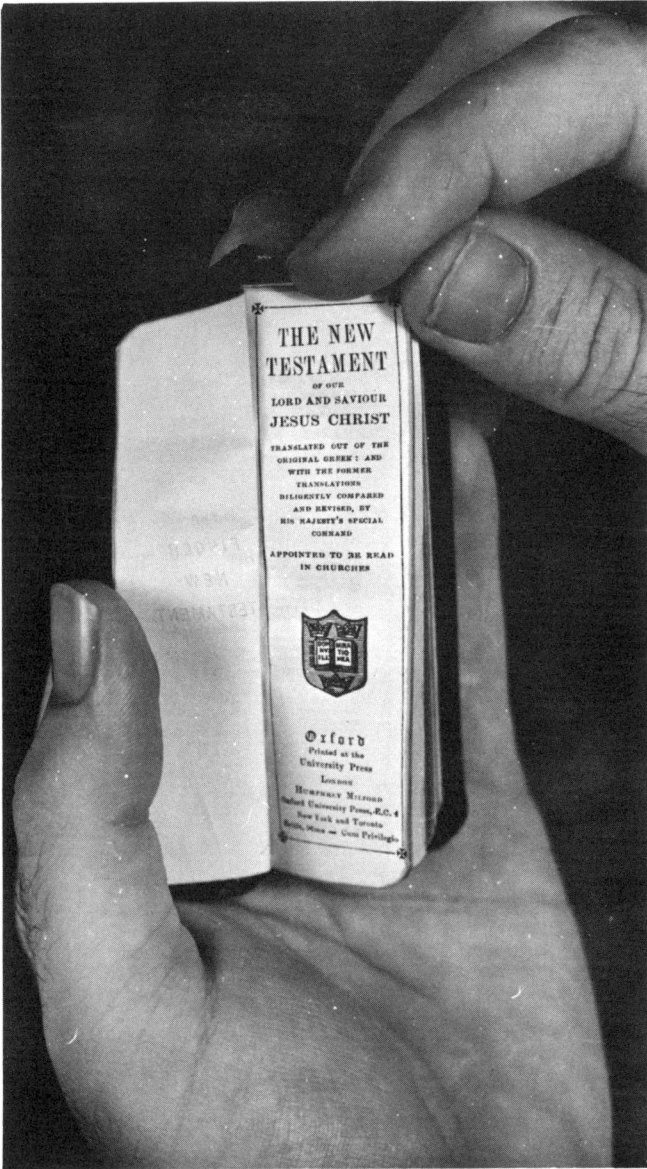

"The Finger New Testament." Oxford: The University Press,
n.d. (55)

90. BIBLIA SACRA POLYGLOTTA. 6 vols. London: Thomas Roycroft, 1655–1657.

The most accurate and best equipped of the early great
polyglots, this one was edited by Brian Walton, later
Bishop of Chester. It offers texts in nine different languages: Hebrew, Latin, Greek, Chaldee, Samaritan,
Syriac, Arabic, Ethiopic, and Persian.

After the Restoration in 1660, Walton added a dedication to Charles II and changed the preface to lessen the
thanks to Oliver Cromwell for assistance. This copy has
that "loyal" preface rather than the "republican," and the
new dedication. Curiously, it even has the dedication in
another and apparently later setting bound in after the
first setting.

(D&M 1446; Wing B2797)

91. NOVUM TESTAMENTUM. Amsterdam: Elzevier Press, 1658.

This volume marks the first issue of the Greek Testament
edited by Curcellaeus for the Elzeviers.

(Parsons copy. D&M 4698)

92. QUATOR D.N. JESU CHRISTI EVANGELIORUM VERSIONES PERAN-
TIQUAE DUAE . . . Dordrechti, 1665.

T. Marshall and F. Junius edited this volume which is the
editio princeps of the Gospels in Gothic.

(D&M 4557)

93. LE NOUVEAU TESTAMENT . . . TRADUIT EN FRANCOIS. 2 vols.
Mons: Gaspard Migeot, 1667.

The first French Port Royal edition, sometimes known as
De Sacy's version from the name of the final translator:
Louis Isaac le Maistre, better known by his assumed name
of De Sacy or De Saci, an anagram of Isaac. Port Royal
was a religious settlement and school at Paris associated
with the Jansenist movement. The hostility of the Sor-
bonne to this Jansenist text forced the Port Royalists to
have their translation printed outside France. Despite the
attribution to Mons on the title page, the volumes were
probably printed by the Elzevier press at Amsterdam. In
1668 the edition was placed on the Index.

(Parsons copy. D&M 3756)

Illustration and text from facing pages of GENESIS. The First
Chapter. London: The Nonesuch Press, 1924. (58)

AND GOD SAID LET THE EARTH
BRING FORTH GRASS THE HERB
YIELDING SEED AND THE FRUIT
TREE YIELDING FRUIT AFTER HIS
KIND WHOSE SEED IS IN ITSELF
UPON THE EARTH AND IT WAS SO
★ ★ AND THE EARTH BROUGHT
FORTH GRASS AND HERB YIELDING
SEED AFTER HIS KIND AND THE
TREE YIELDING FRUIT WHOSE SEED
WAS IN ITSELF AFTER HIS KIND
AND GOD SAW THAT IT WAS GOOD

94. LA SACRA BIBLA; QUAI AIS TOUT LA SANCTA SCRITTURA . . .
Scuol, 1679.

The Bible translated from Hebrew and Greek into Ro-
mansch by Jacob Dorta.

(*D&M 7688*)

95. NOVUM . . . TESTAMENTUM A SEBASTIANO CASTALIONE LATINE
REDDITUM. London, 1682.

This is a reprinting of Châteillon's translation of the Bible.
Sebastian Châteillon (1515–1563) was helped by Calvin
to become rector of a Geneva school; however, he was ex-
pelled in 1544 on theological grounds. He published his
Latin version of the Bible in 1551 from Basel.

Châteillon wanted a Bible which could be understood
by the common people, so at times he would coin his own
words. From 1551 on he was attacked by his former associates in Geneva.

(*D&M 6246*)

96. HEPTATEUCHUS, LIBER JOB, ET EVANGELIUM NICODEMI;
ANGELO-SAXONICE. Oxford, 1698.

This work was translated by Aelfric, abbot of Eynsham.
His preface to Genesis had been previously printed in
Wharton's *Auctarium Historiae Dogmaticae Jacobi Useri*
. . . in London, 1589.

(*D&M 1606; Wing B2198*)

97. THE OLD TESTAMENT. Amsterdam: Immanuel Athias, 1700–
1705.

An edition in Hebrew edited by David Nuñez Torres but
without Rashi's commentary sometimes included. The
binding is of silver elaborately chased with floral and ani-
mal designs and with insets of lace-like silver designs.

(*Wrenn copy. D&M 5140*)

98. NOVUM . . . TESTAMENTUM SYRIACUM, CUM VERSIONE LATINA
. . . Leyden: March 1, 1708.

In this volume the Latin and the Syraic texts are printed in
parallel columns. The Syriac language used in this Bible
is of the "classical" Edessene idiom, belonging to the eastern branch of the Aramaic language. The dialect is still
preserved as the sacred language of several Eastern
Churches. This book is also thought to be the first printed
from stereotype.

(*D&M 8969*)

Title-page from THE HOLY BIBLE. London: The Nonesuch Press, 1924–27. (59)

COMETH JESUS WITH
THEM UNTO A PLACE
CALLED GETHSEMANE, AND
SAITH UNTO THE DISCIPLES, SIT YE HERE, WHILE I
GO AND PRAY YONDER. AND HE TOOK WITH HIM
Peter and the two sons of Zebedee, and began to be sorrowful and very heavy. Then saith he unto them, My soul is
exceeding sorrowful, even unto death: tarry ye here, and
watch with me. And he went a little farther, and fell on his
face, and prayed, saying, O my Father, if it be possible, let
this cup pass from me: nevertheless not as I will, but as thou
wilt. And he cometh unto the disciples, and findeth them
asleep, and saith unto Peter, What, could ye not watch with
me one hour? Watch & pray, that ye enter not into tempta-
tion: the spirit indeed is willing, but the flesh is weak. He
went away again the second time, and prayed, saying, O my

69

Page from THE FOUR GOSPELS. Waltham St. Lawrence at Birkshire: The Golden Cockerel Press, 1931. (60)

99. BIBLIA, THET AR ALL THEN HELIGA SKRIFT PA SWENSKO. Stockholm, 1727–1728. 2 vols.

These are only two volumes of the original six which were printed between 1711 and 1728 in Swedish. It was an annotated edition of the Bible, begun in 1674 by Johannes Gezelius the elder (1615–1690), Bishop of Abo, and completed by his son, Johannes Gezelius the younger (1647–1718), who succeeded his father as a bishop.

(*D&M 1821*)

100. LA SAINTE BIBLE . . . LE TOUT REVEU SUR LES ORIGINAUX, ET RETOUCHÉ DANS LE LANGAGE: AVEC DES PARALLELES ET DES SOMMAIRES PAR DAVID MARTIN. Leipzig: Jonas Korte, 1739.

Martin's version in octavo was intended "pour l'usage de la jeunesse & des Voyageurs."

(*see D&M 3809 for related publication*)

101. LA SAINTE BIBLE . . . SUIVANT LA VERSION ORDINAIRE DES EGLISES REFORMÉES . . . AVEC DES PRÉFACES . . . TIRÉES DE LA BIBLE DE M. MARTIN. Dienne et Yverdon: Heilmann et Neubrand, 1746, 1745.

The general title page is dated 1746 while the New Testament title page is dated 1745. This edition has an engraved frontispiece as well as plates of illustrations.

(*D&M 3815*)

102. NOVUM TESTAMENTUM CUM VERSIONE LATINA ARIAE MONTANI. Leyden, Wetstenius, and London: Johannus Nourse, 1772.

A diglot edition in Greek and Latin. The particular interest of this copy is in its fore-edge painting of—ironically—Vauxhall Gardens, then the fashionable pleasure resort on the south bank of the Thames. A fore-edge painting was made by fanning out the edges of the pages, painting the picture there, and then closing the edges and gilding the ends. The painting shows only when the pages are fanned again. In this painting, the pages may be fanned in either direction to show the same picture.

(*Bachmann copy. D&M under 6256*)

103. BIBLIA . . . NACH DER DEUTSCHEN UBERSETZUNG D. MARTIN LUTHERS. Germantown, [Pennsylvania]: Christohp Saur, 1776.

In 1743 Christoph Saur, a physician of Germantown, printed the first American Bible in a modern language on a press sent to America by German Baptists. On his death in 1758, his son, of the same name, took over the press and issued a second edition in 1763. In 1776 he was just completing a third edition—this one—when the Revolutionary War interrupted the work, and most of the unbound sheets were used to make cartridges. As a result, the edition, a sort of "war edition," is scarce today.

(*Williford copy. D&M under 4240*)

104. SAGRADA BIBLIA, EN LATIN Y ESPAÑOL. 25 vols. Mexico City: Imprenta de Galván, under the direction of Mariano Arévalo, 1831–33.

Apparently the first Bible printed in Mexico, and certainly the first translated into Spanish by Mexicans. Often called the De Vence Bible from the name of one of the editors and commentators of the French edition of 1820–24 from which it was translated, it prints both the Spanish and the Latin Vulgate text.

(*Latin American Collection copy. D&M 8515*)

105. EMBÉO E MAJARÓ LUCAS. BROTOBORO RANDADO ANDRÉ LA CHIPE GRIEGA, ACÁNA CHIBADO ANDRÉ O ROMANÓ, O CHIPE ES ZINCALES DE SESÉ. Madrid, 1837.

The first edition of a translation of *Luke* into Romany by George Borrow (1803–1881). Borrow is known for his travels around much of the world and for his experiences among the Spanish Gypsies.

106. THE NEW TESTAMENT OF OUR LORD AND SAVIOUR JESUS CHRIST, TRANSLATED INTO THE CHOCTAW LANGUAGE . . . New York, 1854.

This is the first re-issue of the translation made by A. Wright and C. Byington which appeared in 1848. The Choctaws were an Indian tribe belonging to the Muskhogean family. They used to inhabit southern Mississippi and western Alabama, but then they settled north of the Red River in Indian territory. In 1890 there were 10,000 pure-blooded members of this tribe.

(*Dienst copy. D&M under 3051*)

THE

HOLY BIBLE

Containing the Old and New
Testaments : Translated out
of the Original Tongues and
with the former Translations
diligently compared and revised by His Majesty's special
Command

Appointed to be read in Churches

OXFORD
Printed at the University Press
1935

Title-page from THE HOLY BIBLE. Oxford, 1935. (61)

107. PARABOLA DE SEMINATORE EX EVANGELIO MATTHAEI IN LEXXII EUROPAEAS LINGUAS AC DIALECTOS. London: By W. H. Billing for Prince Louis-Lucien Bonaparte, 1857.

A "polyglot" of the parable of the sower taken to the ultimate stage: 72 languages and dialects, not including the major modern languages. This is one of the limited editions privately printed for Prince Louis-Lucien Bonaparte, nephew of the emperor, to further the study of languages. There was probably no intention here, as there was of course in the great polyglots, to encourage textual scholarship on the Bible.

(Bachmann copy. D&M 1467)

108. CANTICUM CANTICORUM SALOMONIS QUOD HEBRAICE DICITUR SIR HASIRIM. Weimar: The Cranach Press, 1931.

No. 10 of 200 copies. A striking example of modern illustration by Eric Gill. For obvious reasons, private presses have tended to reprint individual books of the Bible—as this Song of Solomon—rather than complete editions, and many presses have tried their hand at one book or another.

(Hanley copy)

109. THE HAGGADAH. London: [ca. 1939]

The Hebrew word *Haggadah* means "telling." The *Haggadah* developed as the written account for home use of the order of the Passover Eve celebration. The origins for the ritual as it is known today reach back 3,000 years while the framework has been unchanged for over 2,000 years.

During the Middle Ages a tradition of Haggadah-illumination grew up with the best integration of text and ornament coming out of Germany. In this edition the contemporary illuminator, Arthur Szyk, has also tried to closely relate text and art. He has made use of modern types of people readily recognizable to all. This is No. 125 of a limited edition of 125 copies.

פוסח הם עונית ובנבחדות ודברם ואסירם כיגיל

פיכך אנחנו חייבים להודות
לשבח לפאר לרומם להדר
לברך לעלה ולקלם למי שעשה
לאבותינו ולנו את כל הנסים
האלו הוציאנו מעבדות לחרות
מיגון לשמחה ומאבל ליום
טוב ומאפלה לאור גדול
ומשעבוד לגאלה ונאמר לפניו
הללויה הללו עבדי ייי

Page from THE HAGGADAH. London, [ca. 1939]. (109)

IV

THE BOOK OF PSALMS
IN TRANSLATIONS OR WITH
COMMENTARIES BY
DISTINGUISHED AUTHORS

110. DIE SYBEN BUTZ-PSALMEN MIT TEUTSCHER AUSZLEGUNG . . .
DURCH DEN HOCHGELERTEN DOCTOREN MARTINUM LUTHER.
Strassburg: Johannus Knoblouch, 1519.

Luther's German translation and commentary on the seven
penitential Psalms: 6, 32, 38, 51, 102, 130, 143. This fifth
issue was printed from the Leipzig fourth issue and shows
some textual changes.

111. OCTAVVS TOMVS OPER VM DIVI AVRELII AVGVSTINI HIPPONEN-
SIS EPISCOPI, CONTINENS ENARRATIONES IN PSALMOS MYS-
TICOS. Basil: Johann Froben, 1529.

Not only is this a book of commentaries by St. Augustine,
it was printed by Froben, the celebrated printer of Basil
who was connected with Erasmus as well as other promi-
nent men of the age.

112. THE PSALMES OF DAVID AND OTHERS WITH M. JOHN CALVINS
COMMENTARIES. London: by Thomas East and Henry Mid-
dleton for Lucas Harison and George Byshop, 1571.

One of the earliest individual editions of the Psalms in
English designed for scholarly study rather than for sing-
ing or esthetic pleasure. This translation by Arthur Gold-
ing is dedicated to Edward de Vere, Earl of Oxford, and
is the first translation of Calvin's commentaries on the
Psalms.

(*STC 2389*)

Illustration from BIBELIN MED BILER AV REMBRANDT. Stockholm, 1954. (67)

AND IT CAME TO PASS, WHEN JESUS HAD FINISHED ALL THESE SAYINGS HE SAID UNTO HIS DISCIPLES, YE KNOW THAT AFTER TWO DAYS IS THE FEAST OF THE PASS OVER, AND THE SON OF MAN IS BETRAYED TO BE CRUCIFIED.

THEN ASSEMBLED TOGETHER THE ✝ CHIEF PRIESTS AND THE SCRIBES, & THE ELDERS OF THE PEOPLE, UNTO THE PALACE OF THE HIGH PRIEST, WHO WAS CALLED CAIA‑ ‑PHAS, & CONSULTED THAT THEY MIGHT TAKE JESUS BY SUBTILTY, AND KILL HIM. BUT THEY SAID, NOT ON A FEAST DAY LEST THERE BE AN UPROAR AMONG THE PEOPLE

NOW WHEN JESUS WAS IN BETHANY, IN THE HOUSE OF SIMON THE LEPER, THERE CAME UNTO HIM A WOMAN HAVING AN ALABASTER BOX OF VERY PRECIOUS OINTMENT, AND POURED IT ON HIS HEAD, AS HE SAT AT MEAT. BUT WHEN HIS DIS‑ ‑CIPLES SAW IT, THEY HAD INDIGNATION, SAYING, TO WHAT PURPOSE THIS WASTE? FOR THIS OINTMENT MIGHT HAVE BEEN SOLD FOR MUCH, AND GIVEN TO THE POOR. WHEN JESUS UNDERSTOOD IT, HE SAID ✝ UNTO THEM, WHY TROUBLE YE THE WO‑ ‑MAN? FOR SHE HATH WROUGHT A GOOD WORK UPON ME. FOR YE HAVE THE POOR ALWAYS WITH YOU; BUT ME YE HAVE NOT ALWAYS. FOR IN THAT SHE HATH POURED

Facing pages from THE PASSION ACCORDING TO SAINT MATTHEW.

THE LAST SUPPER   l'épreuve d'artiste   Rие van Rогeов 54

Marazion, Cornwall: The Ark Press, 1954. (68)

113. THE WHOLE BOOKE OF PSALMES, COLLECTED INTO ENGLISH MEETER BY THOMAS STERNHOLD, JOHN HOPKINS AND OTHERS, CONFERRED WITH THE HEBRUE WITH APT NOTES TO SING THEM WITHALL . . . London: Printed by John Windet, for the Assignes of Richard Day, 1597.

Other contributors to this volume were William Whittingham, Thomas Norton, William Kethe, Robert Wisdome, John Pullain, and Thomas Bastard. The paraphraser's initials appear at the head of each psalm. This *Book of Psalms* by Sternhold, Hopkins, et. al. originally appeared as part of the 1570 Bible printed at Geneva by John Crispin.

(*see D&M 94; STC 2492*)

114. THE PSALMS (in Hebrew). Amsterdam: Menassah Ben Israel, 1625. [3½ × 2 in.]

Latin translation in miniscule with contemporary hand interleaved.

115. PARAPHRASE DES PSEAVMES DE DAVID, EN VERS FRANCOIS. Paris, 1655.

Antoine Godeau, the Bishop of Venice at one time, did the translation for this edition. He also published a paraphrased version of the New Testament in 1668.

116. PSALTERIUM AMERICANUM. THE BOOK OF PSALMS, . . . BUT ALL IN BLANK VERSE. Boston: by S. Kneeland for B. Eliot, S. Gerrish, D. Henchman, J. Edwards, 1718.

Translation and notes by Cotton Mather (1663–1728), published anonymously. Mather, the American Puritan scholar of his age, was prolific in his publication; at least 444 printed items are known to be his. The first edition.

117. THE PSALMS OF DAVID IMITATED IN THE LANGUAGE OF THE NEW TESTAMENT. BY I. WATTS. London: for J. Clark, R. Ford, R. Cruttenden, 1719.

Isaac Watts (1674–1748) is probably best known today for his many hymns that are still sung. This "imitation" of the Psalms has many of the same fine qualities. The first edition.

(*Wrenn copy*)

118. A TRANSLATION OF THE PSALMS OF DAVID, ATTEMPTED IN THE SPIRIT OF CHRISTIANITY. BY CHRISTOPHER SMART. London: by Dryden Leach for the Author, 1765.

Christopher Smart (1722–1771) was not appreciated in his own time, but is today recognized as a man who transformed his religious mania into great poetry. Shortly before this translation appeared, he had spent some time in the madhouse. The first edition. Formerly H. Buxton Forman's copy.

119. LIVRE CONTENANT LES PRIERES PUBLIQUES, L'ADMINISTRATION DES SACREMENS, ET LES AUTRES RITES ET CÉRÉMONIES DE L'ÉGLISE, SELON L'USAGE DE L'ÉGLISE EPISCOPALE PROTESTANTE DANS LES ETATS UNIS DE L'AMERIQUE; AVEC LE PSEAUTIER . . . New York: Robert Wilson, 1803.

A Book of Common Prayer with pslams published in French by the Protestant Épiscopal Church of the United States of America.

120. PSALMI PENITENTIALES. Hammersmith: Kelmscott Press, 1894.

Transcribed and edited by F. S. Ellis, this selection of paraphrases from Psalms was printed by William Morris at the Kelmscott Press. Morris was concerned with the fact that mass-production which was expanding in his time created little beauty. He gave the last years of his life to producing books which "would have a definite claim to beauty."

(*Bachmann copy*)

3000 copies of
THE HOLY BIBLE
AT THE UNIVERSITY OF TEXAS
have been printed in Linotype Caledonia by
The Printing Division of The University of Texas.
The types shown on the front and back endpapers
have been taken and adapted from items 58 and 60.
The illustrations on the covers, preliminary pages
and this colophon have been taken and adapted
from pages in item 47. The initial letter
on page 5 is from item 30, and that
on page 8 is from item 60.
Design and typography by
Kim Taylor
1967

AND THERE ARE ALSO

WHICH JESUS DID,

BE WRITTEN EVERY ONE,

THE WORLD ITSELF

BOOKS THAT SHOULD BE